Piano Exam Pieces

ABRSM Grade 3

Selected from the 2013 & 2014 syllabus

Name

Date of exam

Contents

Editor for ABRSM: Richard Jones

Other pieces for Grade 3

First published in 2012 by ABRSM (Publishing) Ltd, a wholly owned subsidiary of ABRSM, 24 Portland Place, London W1B 1LU, United Kingdom © 2012 by The Associated Board of the Royal Schools of Music

Music origination by Julia Bovee Cover by Kate Benjamin & Andy Potts Printed in England by Headley Brothers Ltd, The Invicta Press, Ashford, Kent

A:1

Allegro in G

H. 328

C. P. E. Bach
(1714–88)

Carl Philipp Emanuel Bach, the second son of the great Johann Sebastian Bach, was taught by his father and became a professional keyboard player, serving for many years as harpsichordist to Frederick the Great in Berlin. He composed over 350 works for solo keyboard and wrote one of the most influential treatises of the 18th century, *Versuch über die wahre Art das Clavier zu spielen* (Essay on the True Art of Playing Keyboard Instruments; Berlin, 1753–62).

This Allegro also exists as No. 4 of Six Marches (*VI Märche*) for two horns, two oboes, two clarinets and bassoon, published some time after the composer's move to Hamburg in 1767. This gives a clue as to how to characterize the keyboard version. All dynamics, slurs (except in b. 2, left hand) and staccato dots are editorial suggestions only, but all staccato wedges are present in the source.

Source: Brussels, Conservatoire Royal de Musique, 5898; MS copy in the hand of J. J. H. Westphal

AB 3630

German Dance in C

No. 4 from 12 German Dances, Hob. IX/12

A:2

Joseph Haydn
(1732–1809)

A German Dance is a dance for couples in quick triple time, popular in South Germany and Austria in the late 18th and early 19th centuries. Haydn, Mozart, Beethoven and Schubert all wrote many sets of such pieces. The orchestral version of Haydn's *12 deutsche Tänze*, Hob. IX/12, was composed and published in 1792. No. 4 is given here in its authentic keyboard version, which was written in December of that year.

In the first section, the dynamics are taken from the orchestral version; in the second section, they are editorial (b. 8) or present in the source (bb. 10 and 12). The dynamics in the Trio are editorial suggestions only. Slurs in bb. 20, 25 and 27 are authentic; all others are editorial.
Source: autograph MS, Budapest, National Széchényi Museum (Esterházy-Archiv)

A:3

Vivace

First movement from Sonata in A, Op. 5 No. 1

Samuel Wesley
(1766–1837)

The English composer and organist Samuel Wesley showed remarkable musical gifts as a child – he composed an oratorio when only eight years old. As an adult he became one of the leading organists of his day and a major figure in the revival of J. S. Bach's music in England.

This Vivace is selected from the first of Wesley's Sonatas, Op. 5, which were composed in 1794 but not published till 1801. All dynamics are editorial suggestions only, as are the marks of articulation, except for the left-hand slurs in bb. 4, 20 and 24, which are present in the source.

Source: *Four Sonatas and Two Duets for the Piano Forte*, Op. 5 (London, 1801)

© 1985 by The Associated Board of the Royal Schools of Music
Adapted from *English Piano Music, 1780–1800*, edited by Timothy Roberts (ABRSM)

Wiosna

B:1

Fryderyk Chopin
(1810–49)

Wiosna Spring

This Andantino in G minor is Chopin's own piano arrangement of a song called *Wiosna*, which he composed in 1838. Its first line reads: 'The dew glistens, the stream gushes through the fields.' *Wiosna* is one of four folksong-like settings by Chopin of poems that his friend Stefan Witwicki had published in his *Pastoral Songs* (Warsaw, 1830). Chopin's Polish songs were not published till 1857, eight years after his death. *Wiosna* seems to have been popular, as Chopin arranged it for piano on a number of occasions between 1838 and 1848, inscribing it in the autograph albums of his friends.

In this edition, all dynamics are editorial suggestions only, except for the *piano* in b. 1, which is present in the source. The middle part is in the upper stave in the original manuscript. Use of pedal is an editorial suggestion only: it is optional in the exam.

Source: autograph MS (Paris, 1846), Vienna, Gesellschaft der Musikfreunde

B:2

Poco allegro

No. 26 from *100 kleine Studien*, Op. 71

Theodor Kirchner
(1823–1903)

The German composer Theodor Kirchner studied in Leipzig, where he met and was encouraged by Mendelssohn and Schumann. He was then active as an organist and teacher in the Swiss towns of Winterthur and Zurich. During the 1870s and 80s he directed and taught at the Würzburg and Dresden conservatories respectively. His music, written in the tradition of Schumann, includes about a thousand compositions for piano, many of which are short character-pieces.

This beautiful piece demands an expressive touch in both hands, subtle dynamic nuances, and a sensitive use of rubato. The staccatos in bb. 9–12 are editorial suggestions only.

Source: *100 kleine Studien für Klavier*, Op. 71 (Leipzig and Brussels: Breitkopf & Härtel, 1884)

German Dance in A

No. 3 from Three German Dances, D. 972

B:3

Franz Schubert
(1797–1828)

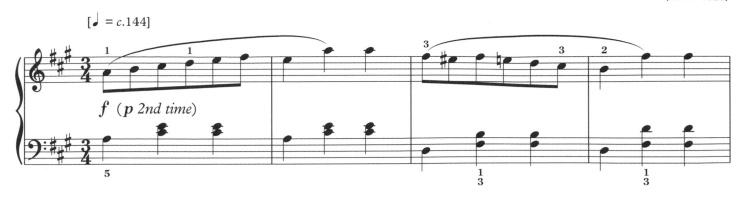

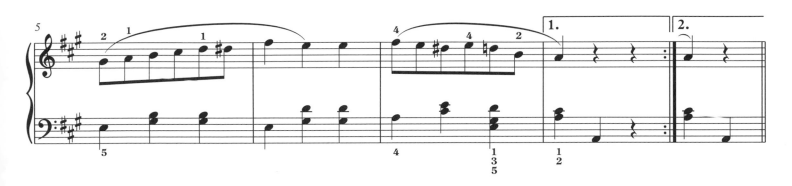

The German Dance is described above under A:2. Many of Schubert's dances, which number over 400, were written for his friends to dance to. Schubert later reused the German dance selected here as the piano part of his song *Hänflings Liebeswerbung* (The Linnet's Wooing), D. 552. This song dates from April 1817, when Schubert was only 20 years old, so the keyboard dance must have been composed before that.
Source: MS copy, Vienna, Gesellschaft der Musikfreunde, Q16190

The Policeman's Song

from *The Pirates of Penzance*

Arranged by Alan Bullard

Arthur Sullivan
(1842–1900)

Arthur Sullivan, one of the most prominent English composers of the Victorian period, studied in London (at the Royal Academy of Music) and at the Leipzig Conservatory. His fruitful collaboration with the writer W. S. Gilbert lasted from 1871 to 1896 and yielded 14 operettas. Sullivan's melodic gifts and Gilbert's witty verse made a winning combination.

'The Policeman's Song' comes from one of the most enduringly popular of their operettas, *The Pirates of Penzance* (1879). The police arrive to arrest the pirates, but are reluctant to do so, hence the song of the sergeant 'When a felon's not engaged in his employments', to which the chorus of constables reply:

When constabulary duty's to be done, to be done,
A policeman's lot is not a happy one, happy one.

Zur Sonnenuntergangsstunde

No. 7 from *Regenbogen Préludes*

Manfred Schmitz
(born 1939)

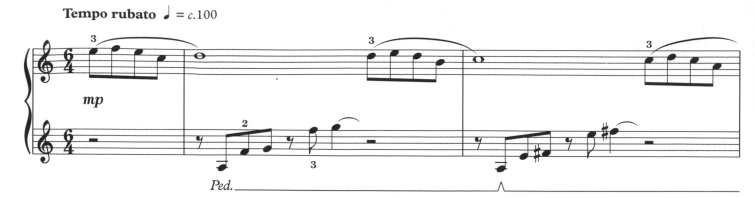

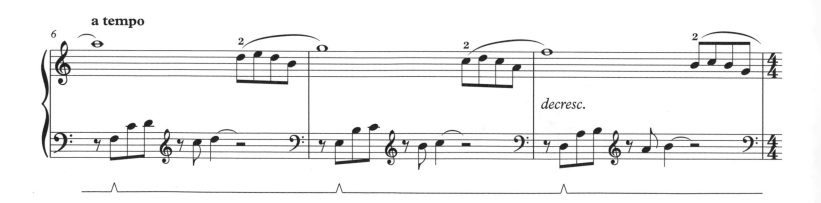

Zur Sonnenuntergangsstunde At Sunset; **Regenbogen Préludes** Rainbow Preludes

Manfred Schmitz studied piano at the Franz Liszt Academy, Weimar, where he later taught. He now works as a freelance composer, pianist and teacher.

Schmitz's collection of preludes is subtitled *21 Träume am Klavier* (21 Dreams at the Piano). He suggests that the pianist should 'savour the sound of the pedal over long stretches of music' and learn the piece by heart in order to 'feel the music and abandon oneself to the spell of its… meditative character.' However, it is not necessary to play this piece from memory in the exam!

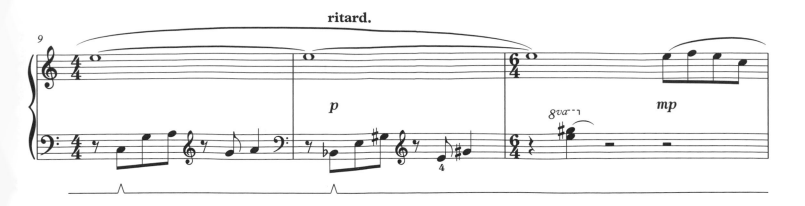

C:3

Blue Sky Blues

No. 1 from *Jazz Jazz Jazz*

Dave Stapleton
(born 1979)

Dave Stapleton studied at the Royal Welsh College of Music and Drama, Cardiff, and is an active composer and jazz pianist. Besides composing for film and television, he aims to unite improvisation, jazz and contemporary classical music. He regularly performs with his jazz group, the Dave Stapleton Quintet, with whom he has recorded three albums.

This blues piece is notable for its inventive, colourful harmonies.